A Family for Sammy

by **KATE GAYNOR**

illustrated by **EVA BYRNE**

Mason County District Library
217 E. Ludington Ave.
P.O. Box 549
Ludington, MI 49431
231-843-8465

Text copyright © Kate Gaynor, 2008
Illustrations copyright © Eva Byrne, 2008

All rights reserved. No part of this publication may be reproduced, stored in or introduced into a
retrieval system, or transmitted in any form or by any means (electronic, mechanical,
photocopying, recording or otherwise) without the prior written permission of both
the owner of the copyright and the publisher of this book.

The names, characters and incidents portrayed in all these works are fictitious. Any resemblance to real persons,
living or dead is purely coincidental.

Published in 2008 by

SPECIAL STORIES PUBLISHING

ISBN 978-095557-870-0

A catalogue record for this book is available from the British Library

Mason County District Library
217 E. Ludington Ave.
P.O. Box 549
Ludington, MI 49431
231-843-8465

Special Stories Publishing

www.specialstories.net

Acknowledgements

Many thanks to Kieran, my father Michael, my brother George and my extended family and friends. Special thanks too to my uncle Liam Gaynor, Liz O'Donoghue, Eva Byrne and the Louth County Enterprise Board for all their help, support and invaluable advice.

A special thanks to social worker Bronagh McKenna and all the foster care team in the Louth H.S.E. Foster care Services Team, Dundalk, Co. Louth and also to Annette O'Malley and the team in the Irish Foster Care Association (I.F.C.A.) Dublin 16.

Special thanks also to Dr. Gerard Molloy Ph.D C.Psychol. whose time and effort with this project was so greatly appreciated.

About the Illustrator

Eva Byrne is a well-known illustrator of books such as "Food to Match Your Mood" "Being You" and "So New York". As well as illustrating book covers, newspaper and magazine articles, she has worked on numerous advertising campaigns both in Europe and the United States. She was delighted to be asked to participate in this very special project with Kate Gaynor.

To read more about the special stories collection, visit the Special Stories website at:
www.specialstories.net

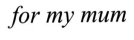

for my mum

Mason County
District Library

Hi! my name is **Sammy**. I am five years old.

It was a day just like today, one whole year ago, that a lady called Sally came to visit me at my house. She was a very kind lady with a big smile and a fluffy red scarf around her neck.

While I ate my lunch, we had a great talk about families and about feelings, like being scared and sad, or happy and safe.

Sally told me that sometimes our mums and dads are not able to take care of us as well as they would like to. She said that when this happens, a boy or girl can feel sad or afraid, which was strange because sometimes that's just how I felt too.

After our talk, Sally told me all about a family who were waiting for a little boy, just like me in fact, to come and stay with them and become part of their family.

Even though I felt sad to be leaving, I was very excited about meeting the family who just couldn't wait to meet me!

On the journey in her bright yellow car, Sally told me that when you go to stay with a new family that you have never met before they are sometimes called a foster family.

When we arrived at the house, I was afraid…

I did not know where I was or what this new family would be like…

As I walked towards the door, the biggest dog I had ever seen ran over to say hello. She licked my face and made me laugh out loud!

When the front door opened, I saw two grown ups with big happy faces and a girl and boy the very same age as me! This was my brand new foster family.

"We're so happy you have come to stay with us Sammy!", said the little girl. On my first day with my new family we had a delicious tea of sausages and big cream cakes. Even Bonnie the big dog had her own plate of sausages.

11

At first I was a little scared of my new home, but my foster care mum and dad were always very kind to me. They had time to help me with my homework and have fun too. So instead of feeling sad and afraid I always felt happy and safe.

My new foster brother and sister were also very kind to me. They showed me their big green playroom where we had great fun playing with all the toys and games.

One day we all took the train to the seaside. We had ice-cream
and played in the sand with our buckets and spades.

It was a happy, happy day!

It wasn't long before Sally came back to visit me in my new home. She told me my mum was looking forward to seeing me again, so we left that very day to go and visit her.

Before I left, I promised Bonnie, the big brown dog, that I'd be back again soon.

Instead of going to my old house, Sally drove to a house I had never seen before. She said that if it was ok with me, I was going to visit my mum here instead. When I finally saw my mum she gave me a big, big hug!

Later that day, Sally took me back to my foster home. But this time I was'nt afraid. I couldn't wait to get back to see my foster mum and dad and tell them all about my day.

So what about you? Do you have a special story like mine?
Why don't you tell me all about it on your Special Story Page?

Your Special Story Page

SPECIAL STORIES PUBLISHING

Kate Gaynor

Notes for Grown Ups on Foster Care

The reasons that children are placed with foster families vary, from neglect, abuse, and violence in the home, to economic reasons. Regardless of the circumstances, entering into foster care is always a very difficult time for the children involved, especially those of a very young age.

Foster Care usually occurs in two main ways: Voluntarily: When a parent or family asks social services for help, and/or a Court order: When a judge decides that it is necessary for the child to be placed in the care of social services.

There are four main types of Foster Care: Day-care, Short-term (1 week to some months) Long-term (a year or more) and Relative (when another family member e.g. grandparents become the foster family).

How to use this book:

Entering into Foster Care can be a very confusing time for any child, with many feeling anxious and afraid about leaving their families behind to live with people they have had little contact with or never met. This book has been designed for parents, teachers, carers and social workers to read with children who are about to begin the process of foster care. The story is told through the eyes of the main character, Sammy, who is himself going through the Foster Care process. He refers to feelings of fear and doubt about going to stay with another family, but he is delighted to find that his 'new' family is kind, caring and has time to have fun with him! By the time Sally the social worker comes to visit him he is feeling happy and safe in his new home.

By reading this story with your child, and discussing the experience of a child in a similar situation, the parent/social worker can enforce the fact that staying with a foster family is a positive thing and not something that children should be afraid of. It also reassures them that they will still have some contact with their birth families.

For information on foster care contact your local foster care association.

Other books from Special Stories Publishing

JOE'S SPECIAL STORY: This story was written to help explain inter-country adoption to young children.

FIRST PLACE: This story aims to help children to understand and accept the effects of cleft palate, cleft lip or any speech impediment in their lives and most importantly, how best to overcome them.

THE WINNER: The intention of this book is to help explain Asthma and its effects to young children.

THE BRAVEST GIRL IN SCHOOL: The objective of this story is to help children with diabetes to appreciate the importance of taking their insulin injections and being aware of what they eat.

THE FAMOUS HAT: The goal of this book is to help children with leukaemia (or other forms of cancer) to prepare for treatment, namely chemotherapy, and a stay in hospital.

THE LOST PUPPY: This book is designed to help young children with limited mobility to see the positive aspects that using a wheelchair can bring to their lives.

To read more about the special stories collection, visit the Special Stories website at:
www.specialstories.net

Macon County
Public Library

Mason County
District Library

MASON COUNTY
DISTRICT LIBRARY
40184989

DISCARD

Mason County District Library
217 E. Ludington Ave.
P.O. Box 549
Ludington MI 49431

16293962R00018

Made in the USA
Middletown, DE
10 December 2014